Monster verse

Monsters in a cap.
Monsters in a cape.
Monster in a hat
that the monsters hate.

This monster has a pet.
His name is Pete.
He likes to be fed
a sack of feed.

Monsters have a bit
and monsters have a bite.
Monsters make a din
when the monsters dine.

This monster had a rod
and down he rode.
To get a cod,
according to the code.

Look at us
and what we can use.
Monster cubs
spell with monster cubes.

Instead of "said"

No monster ever said a thing.
Instead of "said" they wailed and yelled.
"Mine," wailed sister monster loudly.
"Keep out," yelled her monster twin.

Big Monster came
to referee.
“Stop!” she hollered
at the twins.
“What is going on?” she cried,
and waited ’til the shouting died.

Big Monster looked at little monsters.
Little monsters tried again.
“It was not me,” they wailed.
“It was her/him,” they whined.

Big Monster held her hand up.
"Hush, shshshsh!" she called.
"What a noise and hubbub,
what a racket and a fuss."

"Wail, mutter, sob, and moan.
He has my teddy," she complained.
"Hiss, grunt, snarl, and groan.
She has my car," he yelped.

“Give them back,” snapped Big Monster,
“by the time that I count ten.”
“1, 2, 3, 4, 5,” she whispered,
“6, 7, 8, 9, **10**,” she yelled.

Little sister monster twin
gave back the model car.
"Thank you," barked her monster twin
and cried, "so here you are."

Big Monster looked at them and nodded.
"That's better, then," she smiled.
"No more yapping, cackling, snarling.
Do not utter a single sound."

She held up a long pointed finger
and wagged her talon at the twins.
"No more noise and scrapping
or I will send you to your room!"

All was tranquil for some seconds.
Big Monster had just sat down,
when “MINE” cried one little monster twin.
“No mine!” the sister replied.

“That’s it,” snarled Big Monster.
“That’s all that I can take.
I will go up to your room.”
CRASH! The door slammed shut.